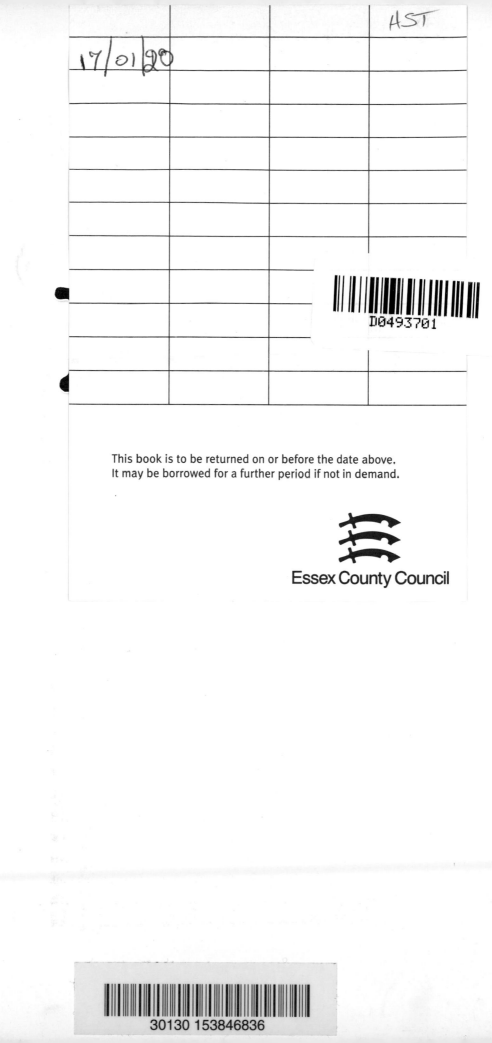

17/01/20   HST

This book is to be returned on or before the date above.
It may be borrowed for a further period if not in demand.

Essex County Council

D0493701

30130 153846836

ESSEX COUNTY
COUNCIL LIBRARY

I am eternally grateful to Euan Kerr, Nick Abadzis, Paul Gravett
and Glenn Dakin for their invaluable help and advice during the
development of Derek the Sheep. Special thanks to Lizzie Spratt,
Natalie Abadzis, Susannah and Thomas Northfield, Dad, Joyce
and family, Ashley Fitzgerald, Matt Abbiss, Dan Green, and my loyal
band of Derek fans for their boundless enthusiasm and support.

This book is dedicated to my wife Julie
G.N.

Bloomsbury Publishing, London, Berlin and New York

First published in Great Britain in 2008 by Bloomsbury Publishing Plc
36 Soho Square, London, WID 3QY

This paperback edition published in 2009

Text and illustrations copyright © Gary Northfield 2008
The moral right of the author/illustrator has been asserted

All rights reserved
No part of this publication may be reproduced
or transmitted by any means, electronic, mechanical, photocopying or otherwise,
without the prior permission of the publisher

A CIP catalogue record of this book is available from the British Library

ISBN 978 1 4088 0428 5

Printed in Malaysia

1 3 5 7 9 10 8 6 4 2

All papers used by Bloomsbury Publishing are natural, recyclable products
made from wood grown in well-managed forests. The manufacturing
processes conform to the environmental regulations of the country of origin

www.bloomsbury.com/childrens

Derek the Sheep

Gary Northfield

A collection of thirteen of Derek's hilarious antics on the farm including *Gone With The Wind* and *There's No Business Like Snow Business*

BLOOMSBURY

LONDON BERLIN NEW YORK

The Grass Is Always Greener

Field Of Dreams

Gone With The Wind

There Ain't No Flies On Me!

It's An Ill Wind

He's Got The Power

One For The Pot

Let's Bee Friends

No Business Like Snow Business

Bad Hair Day

Lame Excuse

Having A Ball

Derek,
a biography

NAME – Derek Sheep esq.

AGE – 12 in dog years. Not sure how that translates into human years. Don't think there's such a thing as sheep years. (I think there are bee years though and Cecil reckons I'm 312 in bee years, but that's just stupid.)

HEIGHT – 3ft 2in.

BUILD – Athletic.

WEIGHT – Quite light. Definitely not fat.

DATE OF BIRTH – April 1st. Although there's nothing remotely funny about it, so don't bother laughing.

PLACE OF BIRTH – Back of a lorry apparently.

FAVOURITE COLOUR – Green. When I'm in my field, I love staring at trees and they're mostly green.

FAVOURITE FOOD – Grass. And hot dogs. And cheese spread sandwiches.

BEST FRIEND – Lenny, although he really gets on my nerves. In fact, everyone gets on my nerves.

PARENTS' OCCUPATION – Mum and Dad retired / on the run. Now living in villa in Costa del Sol after making lots of money selling all of Farmer Jack's top quality hay. I receive occasional postcards and it sounds like they're doing O.K.

Gary Northfield,
a biography

Gary Northfield was born in Romford, Essex in June 1969. He moved to Norfolk when he was two, where he then spent most of his childhood and the bug for writing and drawing funny stories evolved. He moved back to Essex in 1982. Gary graduated from Harrow College (University of Westminster) with a degree in Illustration in 1992. After graduation, he worked in his dad's kitchen furniture factory and an art shop for a few years, during which time he discovered the hidden world of small press (home–made) comics. Finally Gary took the plunge with his own comics in 1999, sporadically creating various titles such as *Great!*, *Little Box of Comics* and *Stupidmonsters*. He acquired the position of 'in–house illustrator' at Eaglemoss Publications in 2002, working on magazines such as *Horrible Histories*, *Horrible Science* and *The Magical World of Roald Dahl*. Gary has been writing and drawing *Derek the Sheep* for DC Thomson's *The Beano* since late 2003.